TRUE PUPPY LOVE

Lola just heard the good news: Mr. and Mrs. Bertram, their neighbors, just bought the little dog they've wanted for so long. Her name is Cinnamon. Lola's parents are happy too because Woofy will have a new friend!

The very minute Woofy saw Cinnamon and her beautiful brown eyes, he fell head over heels in love with her! He is so taken with her that he even forgets to bark and just lies at her feet. Everybody laughs at him, but Woofy isn't laughing at all: being in love is very serious!

Since Cinnamon doesn't seem as attracted to Woofy as he is to her, Lola's dog will have to find his way to her heart. Today he'll bring her the best bone he can dig up. Tomorrow it'll be a flower lying around and the following day, a bandanna he'll have stolen from Lola.

With all these little gifts, attentions and kindnesses, Cinnamon finally starts appreciating Woofy. This greatly amuses Lola and Bugsy, who have been watching them with interest. They're happy to notice that, after a few weeks, Cinnamon gets excited when Woofy shows up and she seems sad when he goes away. Isn't that what love is?

The two lovebirds have been living in perfect harmony for some time when Mr. and Mrs. Bertram make a terrible announcement: they will be moving soon. The Bertrams didn't plan it that way, but Mrs. Bertram had gotten a job offer she couldn't refuse, even though she hesitated at first.

Everyone in the neighborhood is sorry to see the Bertrams go because they're such good neighbors. But no one is as sad as Cinnamon and Woofy. Instead of playing together and enjoying each other's company like before, they now spend their time whining and crying, knowing they will be separated.

Lola just can't watch her dog being so unhappy. He's so low, he doesn't eat anymore. She realizes that she absolutely must think of something. Woofy must become himself again, eat, have fun and spend happy days with Cinnamon again, as they used to until now.

As she talks with the Bertrams, Lola sees there is hope. They tell her that they're moving into a city apartment where they can't have a dog! They thought of leaving her in an animal shelter, but they're very uneasy about that. What they really want is someone to adopt Cinnamon. Yes, better someone in the neighborhood, Lola thinks, so that Woofy will be happy again!

Lola and Bugsy start thinking, because two heads are better than one when you need good ideas. In fact, they only need one idea, but it has to be the right one. I know! Lola says suddenly. All we have to do is ask my parents! Which she does on the spot. One more dog, that won't be any trouble

On the contrary, answer her parents, who don't feel like having two dogs. One is OK, but two is twice the trouble! Lola is very upset. She even starts to panic when the other neighbors don't seem interested. How is Woofy going to react? Lola is almost desperate when she comes up with an idea that could be her last chance.

Mr. Gerry, the policeman... Why didn't she think of him in the first place? He loves Woofy and he's always asking when is Cinnamon going to have puppies! No sooner does she ask him than the deal is done. Mr. Gerry is delighted to adopt Cinnamon, especially if that makes Woofy happy. And Mr. Gerry lives really close, so that's very convenient.

So Mr. and Mrs. Bertram moved away. They were a little heavy-hearted, but relieved to know that Cinnamon was in good hands and would go on seeing Woofy in the park, even on rainy days. Lola's parents can be proud of their daughter! And when Lola and Bugsy see Woofy eating with appetite, they know they found the right solution.